THE

WIZARD'S

HANDBOOK

THE

WIZARD'S

HANDBOOK

by Caroline Tiger

PENGUIN BOOKS

PENGUIN BOOKS

Published by the Penguin Group

Penguin Books Ltd, 80 Strand,
London WC2R 0RL, England

Penguin Putnam Inc., 375 Hudson Street,
New York, New York 10014, USA

Penguin Books Australia Ltd, 250
Camberwell Road, Camberwell, Victoria
3124, Australia

Penguin Books Canada Ltd, 10 Alcorn
Avenue, Toronto, Ontario, Canada M4V 3B2

Penguin Books India (P) Ltd, 11 Community
Centre, Panchsheel Park, New Delhi –
110 017, India

Penguin Books (NZ) Ltd, Cnr Rosedale
and Airborne Roads, Albany, Auckland,
New Zealand

Penguin Books (South Africa) (Pty) Ltd,
24 Sturdee Avenue, Rosebank 2196,
South Africa

Penguin Books Ltd, Registered Offices:
80 Strand, London WC2R 0RL, England

www.penguin.com

First published 2002

1

Copyright © Quirk Productions Inc., 2002

All rights reserved

Illustrations copyright © Headcase Design,
2002

All rights reserved

Designed and illustrated by Paul Kepple
and Timothy Crawford @ Headcase Design,
Philadelphia, Pennsylvania

Made and printed in England by Clays Ltd,
St Ives plc

British Library Cataloguing in Publication
Data

A CIP catalogue record for this book is
available from the British Library

ISBN 0–141–31487–7

PHOTOGRAPHY CREDITS

Pg. ii: Photofest

Pg. vi: Photofest

Pg. 9: (left) Bettmann/CORBIS; (right)
SuperStock

Pg. 10: Scholastic

Pg. 11: The Kobal Collection

Pg. 13: The Kobal Collection

Pgs. 22–23: Photofest

Pg. 26: Photofest

Pg. 31: Roger Wood/Corbis

Pgs. 42–43: Everett Collection

Pg. 48: Photofest

Pg. 56: SuperStock

Pg. 60: SuperStock

Pg. 67: (Nostradamus) Bettmann/Corbis;
(Background) NASA

Pg. 68: (Bulldog) Robert Dowling/
Corbis; (Other Animals) SuperStock;
(Wizard) Richard T. Nowitz/Corbis

Pg. 76: Photofest

Pg. 77: Photofest

Pg. 80: (Books) Michael Freeman/Corbis;
(Wizard) Digital Imagery © Copyright
2001 PhotoDisc, Inc.

CONTENTS

ARE YOU A WIZARD?

When most people think of a wizard, they imagine a tall, thin man with a long, white beard and a pointy hat. Maybe he's standing next to a cauldron, reading through a spell-book, or talking with his black cat. Perhaps he's getting ready to cast a magic spell, or to break a curse that some-one has put on his village. This is the familiar image that we've learned from books and films.

But the truth is, a wizard is anyone with magic inside them, and anyone who believes that magic exists. We all have some level of magical ability, and it can show up in any number of ways. Have you ever dreamed something that eventually came true? That's an example of psychic magic, or fortune-telling. Have you ever seen or heard a ghost? That's an example of spiritual magic, or an ability to communicate with other worlds. Most of us are born with a wizard inside us, but we have to be willing to let the wizard out!

TRADITIONAL WIZARD

FASHIONABLE WIZARD

THE WIZARD INSIDE YOU

You don't need a long white beard to be a wizard. A wizard can be a boy or a girl, thin or fat, with short hair or long hair, with a pointy hat or a cowboy hat or – well, you get the point. Your family cat could be a wizard. Your school principal could be one. Or even your little sister or brother. You could be one too. Take this exam to rate your potential:

NATIONAL WIZARD IDENTIFICATION EXAM
2080-EZ

① Do you like wearing pointy hats?

○ A. Yes
○ B. No
○ C. I never thought about it, but I suppose I would.

② Have you ever dreamed that you were flying?

○ A. Yes, I dreamed I had wings.
○ B. Yes, but I was in an aeroplane.
○ C. No, but I dreamed I could live underwater.

③ Do you understand what animals are saying when they bark, meow, chirp or hiss at you?

○ A. Yes
○ B. What are you, crazy?
○ C. Sometimes

④ Do you like books, films and TV programmes about magic?

○ A. Who doesn't?
○ B. Not on your life.
○ C. Only some of them.

⑤ Do strange things happen when you get really angry, like objects flying across the room or the lights going on and off?

○ A. Yes, these things have happened.
○ B. No, never.
○ C. I've never been angry.

⑥ Do you ever feel like you might be destined for greater things?

○ A. But of course.
○ B. I've never thought about it.
○ C. Yes, but not anything magical.

(7) Have you ever dressed up like a witch, wizard or warlock for Halloween?

○ A. Yes, and I'd do it again!
○ B. No, but my sister or brother did.
○ C. I almost did once.

(8) Have you ever had a dream that ended up being a prediction?

○ A. Yes, that's happened three or more times.
○ B. Yes, that's happened once or twice.
○ C. No, that's never happened, ever.

Add up your points.

(1) a) 3, b) 1, c) 2
(2) a) 3, b) 1, c) 2
(3) a) 3, b) 1, c) 2
(4) a) 3, b) 1, c) 2
(5) a) 3, b) 1, c) 2
(6) a) 3, b) 1, c) 2
(7) a) 3, b) 1, c) 2
(8) a) 3, b) 2, c) 1

YOUR SCORE

8–12 points
Some wizarding potential – it may increase with age

13–18 points
Very strong wizarding potential

19–24 points
Definitely! Yes! A wizard!

No matter how you scored on the National Wizard Identification Exam, you're probably on the right track, because anyone reading this book must have some interest in the world of magic. And if you believe in magic, you know that anything is possible!

Spend some time writing down the reasons you think you might be a wizard. Be sure to note any occurrences that are out of the ordinary. For instance, if you have a dream about flying, write that down. Or if you suddenly understand what a cat is saying when it meows, write that down.

SEVEN REASONS I THINK I MIGHT BE A WIZARD:

1

2

3

4

5

6

7

You may know these wizards by name, but do you know how they discovered their magical talents? This is very important information to know, especially if you're convinced there is a wizard inside *you*.

MERLIN

Just before Merlin's grandfather died, he used his powers to transfer his magical skills to Merlin, who was thirteen years old. And it was a good thing that Merlin acquired these powers when he did, because they ended up saving his life! Soon afterwards, Merlin was handpicked by Vortigern, Britain's king, to be sacrificed. Vortigern's fortress kept falling down for no apparent reason, and his workers were getting tired of rebuilding it. Everyone believed that a sacrifice would please the gods and prevent the castle from falling again.

But Merlin stopped the sacrifice by exercising his visionary power (his ability to see beyond what ordinary people can see) and his power of prophecy (his ability to predict the future). He saw the problem with the fortress did not lie in the building itself. Merlin saw what no one else could see — that the fortress was sitting right on top of an underground pool. And Merlin saw that a red dragon and a white dragon who lived in the pool kept causing the fortress to topple over. He immediately warned Vortigern of the danger.

When Vortigern and his troops looked beneath the fortress, they did indeed find an underground pool with two dragons in it. One was red and one was white, just as Merlin had predicted. Vortigern was so impressed that he set Merlin free.

HARRY POTTER

Perhaps the most famous wizard of our time, Harry was a wizard from birth, but didn't know about his powers until he turned eleven years old and received an invitation to attend the Hogwarts School of Witchcraft and Wizardry. Once he discovered that he was a wizard, all the strange things in his life suddenly made sense. Harry understood why he was able to communicate with a snake at the zoo, for example, and why inanimate objects sometimes flew around him.

Finding out he was a wizard changed Harry's life, of course. He'd been living with a family of Muggles (or humans) his whole life, but when he got to Hogwarts he discovered a completely different world. Some of his classmates had come from whole families of wizards; their houses had magic clocks, and their mothers cooked food using magic (instead of a microwave). Harry even learned how to fly on a broomstick and how to defend himself against the dark arts (magic that's used for evil).

GANDALF

You'll know the name Gandalf if you've ever read J. R. R. Tolkien's book *The Hobbit*, or his fantasy trilogy, *The Lord of the Rings*. Although Tolkien never explained how Gandalf came to be a wizard, it was clear from Gandalf's wise face and his long white beard that he had lived for a long time. And we know that he'd been around for at least 2,000 years because that's how long it took him to put an end to the reign of Sauron.

Tolkien's book *The Hobbit* tells us how Gandalf persuaded a short, hairy creature named Bilbo Baggins to join an expedition to the Lonely Mountain, where a group of adventurers planned to kill a dragon named Smaug. During this quest, Bilbo found the One Ring, a discovery that set the stage for the events described in *The Lord of the Rings*. Throughout these adventures, Gandalf constantly offered wisdom and advice to Bilbo and his companions.

THE 'WIZARD' OF OZ

Everyone knows who this wizard was. Or they do if they've read the book or seen the film that's called — you've guessed it — *The Wizard of Oz*. In the story, the wizard ruled over a magical land called Oz. Everyone in Oz believed that the wizard had great powers. In fact, when someone had a problem, no matter how big or impossible it may have seemed, they went to see the Wizard of Oz.

So Dorothy and her dog Toto, along with a Scarecrow, a Tin Man, and a Cowardly Lion, journeyed to Oz to see if the wizard could solve their problems. To their surprise, they discovered that the great and mighty wizard was not really a wizard after all. He was more of a magician — a person who creates illusions that only *seem* like magic. Still, the 'wizard' helped Dorothy and her friends with all of their problems.

A WIZARD'S INVENTORY

There are a few basic things that a wizard needs to get started. These are tools that wizards have used for centuries, and if they've worked for that long, why change them now?

A MAGIC WAND

Ah, yes. Every wizard has one. And it's easy to make one of your own.

- Just find a twig or a branch. Or go to an ironmongers and ask for a wooden dowel.

- Add something to it that's your own – a hair from your head, a picture of your favourite singer. It can be virtually anything!

- Then decorate the wand with your favourite colours. Tie colourful ribbons around it, or have them coming out of the top so that when you wave the wand around, the ribbons wave with it.

- Paint your wand a solid colour, or decorate it with colourful patterns and designs. If you want a shiny wand, cover it with baking foil. Give it your own personal brand of magic.

- To activate your wand, put it under your pillow for three days and three nights. Before you go to sleep, chant the following words three times into your pillow: 'Wandus Activatus.' At the end of the three days and nights, your wand should be ready to perform magic.

SPELLBOOK

This can be any blank book, from a spiral notebook to a diary. What makes it a spellbook is what you choose to write inside it.

- Write out the spells that you make up.

- Write down the list of ingredients that you will need for a potion.

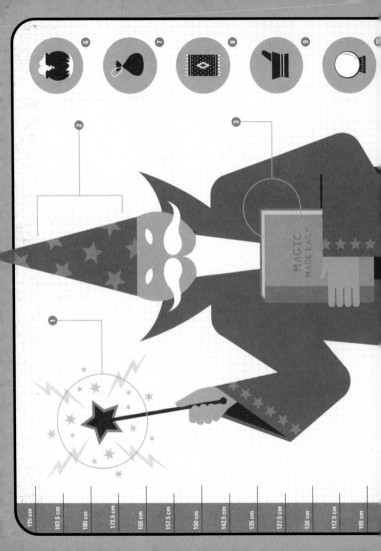

MAGIC
MADE EASY

195 cm
187.5 cm
180 cm
172.5 cm
165 cm
157.5 cm
150 cm
142.5 cm
135 cm
127.5 cm
120 cm
112.5 cm
105 cm

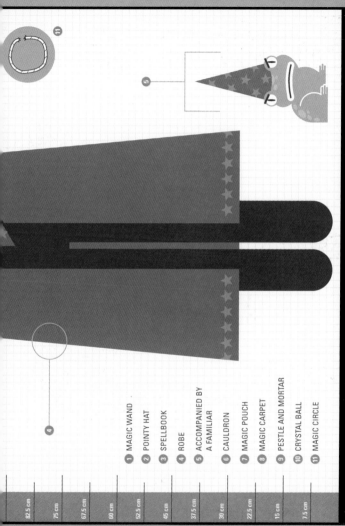

WIZARD CHARACTERISTICS: THEY ARE ABLE TO PREDICT THE FUTURE AND CAST SPELLS FOR GOOD OR EVIL.

1. MAGIC WAND
2. POINTY HAT
3. SPELLBOOK
4. ROBE
5. ACCOMPANIED BY A FAMILIAR
6. CAULDRON
7. MAGIC POUCH
8. MAGIC CARPET
9. PESTLE AND MORTAR
10. CRYSTAL BALL
11. MAGIC CIRCLE

82.5 cm
75 cm
67.5 cm
60 cm
52.5 cm
45 cm
37.5 cm
30 cm
22.5 cm
15 cm
7.5 cm

- You can also write about the kinds of things you'd like to use your spells for, like casting a spell on your broccoli so it disappears from your plate, or bewitching your memory so it retains the formulas you need to pass your maths test.

A MAGIC CIRCLE

This is the place where you'll go to perform your magic, or even just to think about it.

- Find a place that's quiet and private, a place where people are unlikely to disturb you while you're at work. It's important that your magic circle is a place where you can concentrate completely, without any fear of interruption.

- This place can be anywhere, from your bedroom to your kitchen. Attics and basements are good, spooky spots, and may contain spiders or snakes, which are both good helpers. Outside places work well too, if you know of a clearing in the woods or if your back garden is relatively private.

- Map out your circle with a piece of string. The circle should be large enough for you to sit cross-legged in the middle. Walk around the outside, clockwise, with your wand pointing in front of you. Imagine a white light coming from the tip of your wand, drawing a circle in the air, and then chant the following: 'This right here is my magic circle. Whoever strays close will be turned purple.'

ROBE AND HAT

It's a good idea to wear a wizard's robe and pointy hat while you're doing magic.

- The robe can be a floor-length bathrobe or a sheet thrown over your shoulders. Wearing a robe will link you to the thousands of wizards who have come before you, and it will lend you some of their powers.

- A pointy hat is easily made by twisting a large piece of paper, until it makes a cone that fits your head, and taping it so it keeps its shape. You can also decorate your hat the same way that you decorated your wand. (Remember to remove this magical clothing when you leave your magic place!)

OTHER TOOLS

Here are a few more things that you may need at some point, and suggestions for finding them around the house:

- **Cauldron** (to mix potions): Ask your mum or dad for an old cooking pot or mop bucket.
- **Magic pouch** (to hold powders and herbs for potions): A re-sealable plastic bag would work well.
- **Magic carpet or broom** (to fly!): Magic carpets should be small – about the size of a welcome mat. Any broom, or even a sponge mop, will do.

- **Pestle and mortar** (to grind ingredients for potions): If you don't have a pestle and mortar, use the flat side of a spoon and a bowl to mash powders for your potions.

- **Crystal ball** (to see the future): Wizards use crystal balls, but you can also see the future in reflective surfaces – not something as reflective as a mirror, but a recently polished tabletop would do.

A WIZARD'S PHILOSOPHY

A wand, a book, a broom – these are all things you can hold in your hand. But how about invisible things, like curiosity or a sense of humour? Here are some invisible, but equally important, wizard necessities:

- An open mind is vital when a wizard is faced with a creature he's never seen before or powers she never knew she had. For instance, if you were taking a walk

TOO TALL

TOO SILLY

TOO FLOPPY

TOO SMALL

TOO TACKY

PERFECT!

THOUGH WIZARD HATS ARE AVAILABLE IN MANY

YLES, FASHION-SAVVY WIZARDS PREFER THE SHINY SKULL CAP.

one day and met a five-headed snake, would you shake your head and tell yourself you were seeing things? Or would you ask, 'Hey, snake, where'd you get all those heads?'

- A good imagination comes in handy when you're creating spells.

- A desire to help people has long been a tradition among wizards.

- A desire to fight evil is really important. As a wizard, you will acquire certain powers, and you have a responsibility to use them well.

HOW TO RECOGNIZE A FELLOW WIZARD

Since most wizards don't look like Merlin or Gandalf, it's difficult to spot them – but if you're observant, you'll start to recognize subtle clues. Here are some traits you can look for:

- A loyal pet – especially spiders and snakes.

- Solitary behaviour (this gives them time to spend in their magic circles).

- Extensive knowledge of history (since they may know wizards who are hundreds of years old).

- Impatience. Wizards are used to getting whatever they want, as soon as they can imagine it!

- A scent of magical herbs and oils (instead of ordinary kid smells, like crisps and dirty socks).

1. SORCERESS CASTING A SPELL
2. 3. KEEP HANDS RAISED FOR BETTER RESULTS
4. SPELLS SOMETIMES GENERATE ELECTRICITY OR LIGHTNING

CREATING AND CASTING SPELLS

Spells come in many forms. They usually involve words, sometimes combined with pictures and music, and at other times potions with powders and herbs. A spell can be cast for any wish a wizard may have.

WORD SPELLS

The simplest spells are made up of words. They usually rhyme, like a poem, but they don't have to rhyme in order to work. Most importantly, the spell needs to be straight-forward and sincere – the wizard casting it should be absolutely sure he or she wants the results to occur.

There is no rule for the number of words in a spell. It can be made up from anywhere between one short

NONSENSE WORDS

Words that mean nothing, but which sound magical, are also used in word spells. Stick one of these words into your spell when you need a space-filler:

- Gobbledygook
- Gobbledygack
- Abracadabra
- Piddlypoop
- Smacketywack
- Allakazaam

sentence to one-hundred long ones. Of course, longer spells are very complex and not the domain of beginner wizards, so it's best to start with short ones. A two-line spell is a good place to begin.

Here is an example of a word spell that calls for a sunny day:

Tomorrow is Sunday and I wish to play,
Let sunshine come out and rule the day.

Try your hand at spell-writing by filling in the words that are missing from these unfinished spells:

Mother's Day is the end of this week,
A perfect gift is what I _____.

Chocolate is good, chocolate is sweet,
Let today bring me this _____.

Oh magic true, oh camera candid,
Show me where my Frisbee _____.

Did you guess 'seek,' 'treat' and 'landed'? Then you're ready to start creating some of your own spells. First, decide what you want to accomplish. Think of your wishes and dreams. Then start by crafting some short sentences that ask for what you'll need to make your wish come true. Again, the sentences don't have to rhyme, but they're more fun to say if they do. Use the blank pages at the back of this book to write down your spells. Write them with a red pen so they look like ancient spells, which were written with dragons' blood.

A CLASSIC SPELL

Virgil, who lived in ancient Rome, is most famous for writing the *Aeneid*, an epic poem. But what many people don't know is that Virgil was thought to be a wizard by the people of Naples, the town where he lived. They claimed that he conjured up a magical brass fly which buzzed around the town, scaring all the other insects away. We have no way of knowing what the spell sounded like – but it probably had a lot of buzzing in it!

WORDS **THAT RHYME**

To help you along with your spells, consult this list of words that rhyme.

Rhymes with 'cat'	**Rhymes with 'me'**
• baby-sat	• chimpanzee
• fruit bat	• Christmas tree
• muskrat	• honeybee
• sun hat	• jealousy
• acrobat	• silvery
Rhymes with 'levitate'	**Rhymes with 'who'**
• activate	• how-do-you-do
• illuminate	• tap shoe
• leaky crate	• Timbuktu
• paperweight	• overgrew
• tent mate	• witches' brew

Rhymes with 'seat'	Rhymes with 'white'
• smelly feet	• delight
• sweet	• fistfight
• upbeat	• dynamite
• field of wheat	• frostbite
• yummy treat	• goodnight

PICTURE SPELLS

Drawing a picture of what you seek is an excellent way of enhancing your spell. This can be done in the same way you'd draw an ordinary picture. Use a crayon on a piece of rough paper, or use a pen or pencil and a notebook. You could even make a collage by cutting and pasting images from magazines on to a sheet of cardboard.

A picture spell makes a word spell stronger. For example, think back to the Frisbee Finder word spell on page 30:

Oh magic true, oh camera candid,
show me where my Frisbee landed.

To translate this into a picture spell, just draw a picture of the Frisbee in mid-air, floating into the woods. You can even include yourself, standing on the ground and looking up. Add as many details as possible; if you remembered seeing any animals or flowers that day, for example, you should use them in the picture.

YOUR PICTURE SPELL AT WORK

- Once you're finished with your picture, bring it to your magic place.

- Make a magic circle – an invisible circle that concentrates your powers in one place (see instructions on page 18).

- Sit in the circle and say your word spell while you wave your magic wand over the picture.

- Wait for the magic to happen!

With picture spells, it's important to choose colours carefully, and remember what forces they symbolize. With the Frisbee Finder picture spell, for example, you might want to use a lot of yellow, because yellow symbolizes clarity. Here is a chart that will help you understand colours and their powers.

Yellow: clarity, happiness	**Blue:** peace, tranquility
Red: energy, passion	**Purple:** money, power
Green: healing, nature	**Orange:** creativity, imagination
Pink: love, friendship	

FIVE SPELLS JUST FOR YOU

What happens if you need magical assistance, but don't have time to create an original word or picture spell? Just use one of these trusty favourites – they work every time.

1. GOOD-FORTUNE SPELL

Everyone has bad days – and some people even have bad weeks or months! If you want to turn your luck around, use your wizardry powers to bring good fortune into your life.

What You'll Need:

- A crystal (found in department stores), or any shiny, smooth rock from a stream

- Three bowls that fit inside each other (one small, one medium, and one large)

Put the crystal inside the smallest bowl. Then put that bowl inside the medium-sized bowl, and then put those bowls inside the largest bowl. Pour water over the crystal until it just overflows into the medium bowl. Now, wave your magic wand over the crystal and say:

Like anyone else on this land we call Earth,
I've had good and bad luck since the day of my birth.
But one thing's for sure, and I'll say it right here:
This one has been a really bad year.

Now pour more water into the medium-sized bowl so it just overflows into the large bowl. Hold your magic wand, look at the crystal, and concentrate hard while you chant:

Good fortune wash over me,
As water flows into the sea.

POOF!

2. LOVE SPELL

This spell will not make a specific person love you. Rather, it can be used to help bring the right person into your life.

What You'll Need:

- A torch

- Sugar

- Paper and a red pen

- A ball of wool

This only works at night, and you may want to do this spell over a piece of newspaper or a mat, because it does get a little messy. First, turn off all the lights, switch on the torch and place it on the table. Then, write your name in red ink on a piece of white paper. Place the piece of paper beside the torch and sprinkle sugar over the paper and around the torch so that you've made an unbroken circle of sugar.

Concentrate on the beam of light and say:

I'm pretty content with the friends in my life,
And I'm not asking now for a husband or wife,
But it's time, I think, for someone sweet:
A special person from their head to their feet.

(continued on next page)

2. LOVE SPELL

(continued from previous page)

Now take the ball of wool and unravel it completely, all the time thinking about the kind of person you want to come into your life. Do you want a person with a good sense of humour? An athlete? Someone who's good at listening? When the ball is fully unravelled, start pulling it back towards you while you repeat the charm above. When the ball is full again, place it next to the torch and say:

Let love sweeten my days,
As sugar does for doughnut glaze.

3. SELF-IMPROVEMENT SPELL

Do you ever wish you were a better athlete, or a better student, or just a better person in general? This spell can help you be more like the people you admire.

What You'll Need:

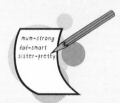

mum-strong
dad-smart
sister-pretty

- A pen and paper

- A small mirror

Write down on the piece of paper the ten people that you admire most. These people can be classmates from school, or celebrities whom you've only seen on television. Opposite the names, write down the qualities you like about those people. Sitting in the middle of your circle, look into the mirror and repeat the ten qualities that you wrote down. Now close your eyes and imagine yourself having all of those qualities.

MANY ADVANCED WIZARDS PREFER TO CAST THEIR WORD SPELLS IN TH

4. PEACE SPELL

This is a good spell for when you're in a fight with some-one – a friend or a sister or a brother – and you want the fight to be over.

What You'll Need:

- A pen and paper

- String

- Sugar

- A bowl

Write down your name and the other person's name on two separate pieces of paper. Roll the papers up together and tie them with a piece of string. Now stick the rolled-up pieces of paper into a bowl of sugar so that they're completely submerged. Wave your magic wand over the bowl and say:

It doesn't matter what the fight was about,

Maybe you tried to steal my trout,

Or borrow my jacket,

Or [say here what the fight was about].

All I know, is the fight's gone too long,

So end the fight now. Can't we just get along?

POOF!

5. MONEY SPELL

Since wizards are always helping people, they sometimes run a little short on cash. If you want to make your wallet a little fatter, give this spell a try. Who knows? Maybe you'll get a raise in your pocket money!

What You'll Need:

• A piece of white paper

• A piece of green paper

• Scissors

• A pen

• Glue

• Green glitter

Draw a star on the piece of white paper. Then cut it out and lay it over the green paper, using the white star to trace. Cut out the green star. Write in the middle of the star how much money you need and what you need it for: '£10 for a book', '£20 for a sweater'. Hold your hands, palms down, over the star and say:

> *I hate to be thought of as greedy,*
> *But now I'm especially needy.*

Now put a thin layer of glue all over the star, and while you're sprinkling the green glitter over it, say three times:

> *Bring me treasure vast and full.*

Now, before the glue dries, fold the star over so that the points meet and say:

> *I seal the magic.*

DISHES

SALT & PEPPER

LEMON

BONES

PAINTBRUSH

RAISINS

SODA WATER

CHAPTER THREE

HOUSEHOLD ILLUSIONS

Part of the fun of being a wizard is being able to astound people by doing things they've never seen before. How many people have seen a raisin dance? Or a rubbery bone? Or invisible ink that delivers a secret message? Here are some magic tricks you can easily do with common objects around the house. And remember: A wizard never reveals the secrets of magic, no matter how often people ask!

RAISIN LEVITATION

What You'll Need:

- A glass

- Soda or fizzy mineral water

- Vinegar

- Baking soda

- Raisins

- Your magic wand

- (Optional: robes and a pointy hat)

Fill a glass nearly to the top with the water. Add ⅓ to ¼ cup of vinegar and two teaspoons of baking soda. Stir gently. Now drop some raisins into the glass. Wave your magic wand over the glass and shout, 'Wrinklus Levitatimus!' The raisins will start to bounce up and down, as if they're dancing.

BENDY BONES

What You'll Need:

- A bowl
- Chicken drumstick bones
- Vinegar
- Your magic wand
- (Optional: robes and a pointy hat)

The next time you have chicken for dinner, save two or three drumstick bones for this trick. Put them in a bowl and pour enough vinegar into the bowl so that the bones are covered. Now wave your magic wand over the bowl and say, 'Hardness Vanishmus!' One week will pass before the magic takes effect – but when you remove the bones from the vinegar, they'll be soft and rubbery. Try to bend them!

STATIC CLING-ON

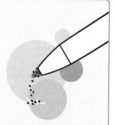

What You'll Need:

- A small plate or saucer

- Salt

- Pepper

- A plastic pen

- Felt or wool

Sprinkle a little salt and pepper on a plate and swirl it together with a fingertip. Rub the pen against the felt or wool. Now, hold the pen very close to the salt-and-pepper mixture and move it around slowly. Say, 'Pepper Grains Levitatimus!' The pepper will jump up to the pen, but the salt will stay behind.

INVISIBLE INK

What You'll Need:

- A fresh lemon
- A watercolour paintbrush
- A piece of paper
- An adult helper

Squeeze the fresh lemon into a bowl. Dip the paintbrush into the juice and use it to write a message on a piece of paper. (You can use your finger if there's no paintbrush handy.) Since lemon juice is transparent, you won't be able to read your message. Now ASK AN ADULT to take the piece of paper and put it in the oven at 180 degrees for ten minutes. While you wait, recite these magic words ten times: 'Letterus Lemonus Reappearicus!' The heat will make the 'ink' visible so that when you take it out, your message will be visible too!

PRESTO PATTERN

What You'll Need:

- Petroleum jelly (like Vaseline)
- A glass plate
- A plastic cup

Make a pattern on the glass plate using the petroleum jelly, or write something simple, like your first name. Fill the plastic cup with warm water and place it in the freezer next to the plate that you've just drawn on with the jelly. As soon as you close the freezer door, recite the magic words: 'Letterus Jellyus Reappearicus!' Within an hour or two the water vapour will condense and freeze on the non-jellied parts of the plate, forming frost and revealing your design!

Now that you've convinced everyone that you really are a wizard, see if they want you to predict their futures.

ABRACADABRA ATTITUDE

Part of the fun of creating illusions for an audience is to see peoples' reactions. Their mouths hang open, their eyes pop, and they may say things like 'No way!' Though wizards shouldn't really flaunt their powers, it's only natural that a young wizard who's just starting out may want to prove himself or herself to unbelieving friends. If that's true of you, then consider spicing up your act a little with an assistant, or by wearing a cape and saying things like 'Abracadabra!' This makes the illusions seem even more exciting than they already are.

CHAPTER FOUR

PREDICTING THE FUTURE

One talent that wizards share is the ability to divine, or see, the future. One ancient wizard named Alessandro di Cagliostro, who lived in the 1700s, used these powers to make a fortune in the lottery! But that's not a very admirable way to use your powers. Rather, you decide to tell someone's fortune if that person is in trouble, or if you think that they may need help.

Dreams, omens, crystal balls, bibliomancy, and cleromancy are all ways of predicting the future that have been around for thousands of years. Seeing the future is a special kind of magic, because it allows wizards to prevent bad things from happening. Imagine if you could predict that a bird dropping was going to land on your head while you were playing outside tomorrow. Then you could avoid being in that spot!

If there's a particular question about the future that you need to answer – such as 'Will I ever get married?' or 'What will I do when I grow up?' – try concentrating on that question for a minute or two before you begin any of these methods.

BIBLIOMANCY

The prefix of bibliomancy – biblio – indicates that it has something to do with books. And so it does. Many famous wizards have been known to predict the future by opening a book at random and letting their index finger fall on a passage of words. These words are then taken as an omen. You can try this with any book – from the dictionary to your favourite novel.

CHOOSING THE RIGHT BOOK

Say you have a friend who wants to know if he'll be good enough to get into the football team. You can answer his question through bibliomancy. There are different methods for choosing the book you'll use, but most wizards select the book at random: Plant yourself in front of a bookcase, close your eyes and stick out your hand. Whichever book your hand lands on is the one you'll use. Even a cookbook will work, but you'll have to ponder how the passage relates to your question about football.

Another alternative is to choose a book that's related to the question you're asking. Maybe you'll choose a novel about a football player, or pick a book about football

statistics. If you turn to a passage about Michael Owen, we're pretty sure your friend will make the team!

CRYSTAL BALLS

Crystal balls are an excellent way of predicting the future, and wizards have used them since the beginning of time. Although a normal person will peer into a crystal ball and see a crystal ball, a wizard can actually witness scenes from the future. It's a little like watching television – only without the ad breaks! Crystal balls can be very expensive, so beginner wizards may choose to start out by peering into crystal rocks, which can be found while camping or hiking.

CLEROMANCY

Cleromancy involves objects – usually dice, stones, bones, or dried beans – and the patterns they fall into when you throw them on the ground. Bantu-speaking wizards in

South Africa use the knuckle bones of goats or wild boars, but you can use any objects that are handy. Use at least five of the same kind of object. The important part is to notice the pattern they make.

- **A straight line:** You are on the right path.
- **A zigzag:** You are not afraid to take risks.
- **A circle:** You will have many close friends.

OMENS

Omens are another method that wizards have for telling someone's fortune or for seeing the future. One well-known omen is a black cat crossing your path. This is said to mean that something bad is going to happen. Seeing a rainbow is an example of a good omen. The trick with omens is keeping an eye out for them. It's also important to listen to your intuition, or that voice inside you that speaks up when you're in a dangerous spot. If something

CAN YOU WORK OUT WHICH OF THE FOLLOWING OMENS ARE GOOD OR BAD?

① **A HAILSTORM**

② **RECEIVING AN UNEXPECTED GIFT**

③ **FINDING A FOUR-LEAF CLOVER**

④ **DROPPING A FORK**

⑤ **LEAVING A DOOR OPEN**

⑥ **SEEING A THREE-LEGGED DOG**

ANSWERS: (1) **Bad** (hailstones are harmful); (2) **Good** (an unexpected gift means someone is thinking well of you); (3) **Good** (a four-leaf clover is a symbol of good luck); (4) **Bad** (when you drop a fork, it can't be used until it's clean again); (5) **Good** (when you leave a door open, you're inviting good tidings into your house); (6) **Bad** (a three-legged dog has probably been in an accident).

MAKE YOUR OWN DREAM PILLOW

YOU WILL NEED:

- Two 30cm by 20cm pieces of cloth
- A needle and thread
- Herbs and/or oils

HERE ARE SOME ORDINARY KITCHEN HERBS YOU CAN USE IN YOUR DREAM PILLOW:

- Rosemary or cedar (to avoid nightmares)
- Cloves (retrieve buried memories)
- Bay laurel (for inspiration)
- Marjoram (lifts sadness)

THE FOLLOWING CAN BE FOUND AS OILS. PUT A FEW DROPS IN YOUR DREAM PILLOW TO ACTIVATE THEIR MAGIC:

- Lilac (to recall past lives)
- Lavender (for relaxing deep sleep)
- Jasmine (to increase psychic awareness)

1. Gently mix your herbs and oils together in a bowl. You don't have to use all of the ones listed here – two or three is enough.

2. Lay one of the two pieces of cloth on top of the other and stitch the two 20cm sides and one of the 30cm sides. Your stitching should begin 3cm from the edge.

3. Transfer your mixture of herbs and oils from the bowl to the pouch you've made. Do not overfill the pouch – it will be too lumpy for you to sleep on.

4. Stitch the last side. Voilà – a dream pillow! Tuck it inside your pillowcase for sweet dreams.

makes you shiver or makes the hairs on the back of your neck stand up, it's probably a bad omen. The more omens you see, the better you'll get at being able to tell which are good and which are bad.

DREAMS

Sometimes, a vision comes in a dream and you don't realize it was a vision until it comes true. Even expert wizards admit that dream visions are hard to remember the next day, because memories of our dreams fade so quickly. It's a good idea to keep a blank notebook next to your bed so that you can record your dreams when they're still fresh in your mind.

NOSTRADAMUS

From the human flock nine will be sent away,
Separated from judgment and counsel:
Their fate will be sealed on departure
Kappa, Thita, Lambda the banished dead err.

This is one of many 'quatrains' (verses made up of four lines) that Michel Nostradamus wrote. This French doctor and astrologer lived in the 1500s and is considered by many to have been a wizard. Some say Nostradamus predicted the invention of bombs, rockets, submarines and aeroplanes – all of which were invented many centuries after his death. Many believe that the above quatrain predicted the explosion of the *Challenger* space shuttle in 1986. The shuttle burst into flames just seconds after its departure ('Their fate will be sealed on departure'), and the problem was blamed on a faulty part made by a company called Thiokol (which, believers point out, is close to 'Thita'). Sceptics respond by stating there were seven astronauts on board, not nine. Are you a believer or a sceptic?

THE
AEROPLANE IS
INVENTED
(1903)

NUCLEAR
BOMBS ARE
INVENTED
(1945)

WORLD
WAR II
(1939)

THE
CHALLENGER EXPLODES
(1986)

CHAPTER FIVE

ANIMALS AND MAGIC

Wizards have a different word for their pets – they call them their 'familiars'. (The word 'familiar' comes from the Latin word 'famulus', which means 'attendant.') Cats are very popular familiars because many people believe they have magical powers. In fact, some people believe that cats are actually wizards in disguise. To a wizard, a cat is a helper in magic, not just a pet to cuddle and feed.

FINDING YOUR OWN FAMILIAR

Other animals, besides cats, that make good familiars are owls, frogs, toads, dogs, mice and guinea pigs. All are believed to possess some magic and could make good attendants for any wizard. Although it's helpful to have cat, dog and guinea pig familiars working in your house, it's also acceptable to visit owls, frogs and other outdoor animals in their own environments.

Chances are, you already know the animal that would be the ideal familiar for you. What's your favourite animal? What stuffed animals do you have? Is there a certain animal that you love learning about in science lessons or that you think is really cool? That's probably your familiar.

Having your familiar near by increases your power. If it's an animal that's nearly impossible to see every day, like a dolphin or an elephant, then keep some pictures of it in your magic place. On the next page are some animal familiars and traits you might share with them.

Familiars aren't the only animals that wizards associate with. They also find themselves working with magical animals, like dragons and unicorns, which can be incredibly helpful for any wizard on a major adventure.

DRAGONS

Dragons developed their reputation for wickedness long ago. These creatures have always been very fierce, but they're not exactly the smartest animals. Maybe that's why it's so easy for evil wizards to cajole dragons into guarding their treasures or their kidnapped princesses. Dragons make very good security guards because not many creatures can fight them and win. Hard scales protect a dragon's body like a coat of armour, and their long fangs, sharp claws and heavy, thumping tails are effective in

FAMILIARS AND THEIR TRAITS

1. **DOG:** FAITHFULNESS, STRENGTH
2. **TIGER:** ADVENTURE
3. **RAT:** SHREWDNESS
4. **SEAGULL:** RESPONSIBLE BEHAVIOUR
5. **BEAR:** SWIFTNESS
6. **SWAN:** BEAUTY
7. **CAT:** INDEPENDENCE
8. **ELEPHANT:** STRENGTH
9. **SNAKE:** CHARM
10. **DOLPHIN:** INTELLIGENCE
11. **EAGLE:** GREAT SIGHT AND PERCEPTION
12. **OWL:** SILENT WISDOM
13. **SEAL:** IMAGINATION
14. **MOUSE:** ATTENTION TO DETAIL
15. **HORSE:** LOVE OF FREEDOM AND TRAVEL
16. **ALLIGATOR/CROCODILE:** FEROCIOUSNESS
17. **FROG:** ADAPTABILITY
18. **RABBIT:** CREATIVITY
19. **BUTTERFLY:** JOY
20. **TURTLE:** STEADFASTNESS

combat. They all have long, monstrous wings, and some have the ability to fly.

There are many types of dragon. They come in all sizes and shapes and can be many different colours. The hydra, a dragon killed by the Greek hero Hercules, had nine heads. Every time Hercules cut one off, another would grow in its place! The largest dragons are said to live in Greenland and Russia.

On the other hand, there are many friendly dragons too – like Puff, the Magic Dragon, who a music group called Peter, Paul and Mary sang a song about. In the song, Puff befriends a little boy named Johnny.

So, how can you recognize a friendly dragon? As you'll see by this chart, it's not that difficult. The differences between a friendly and a hostile dragon are very obvious. (What no one knows is what makes a friendly dragon turn evil!)

THE FRIENDLY DRAGON	THE HOSTILE DRAGON
● breathes air	● breathes fire
● makes friendly noises, like a puppy, but louder	● growls and roars
● invites you into his cave	● won't let you near his cave
● uses tail to help you lift heavy things	● uses tail to knock over houses and buildings
● often kneels down to let you jump on his back	● often rears up on his hind legs and flares his nostrils when he sees you coming

FORCES OF GOOD: ① FRIENDLY WIZARD ② MAGICAL UNICORN

FORCES OF EVIL: ③ EVIL WIZARD ④ HOSTILE DRAGON

UNICORNS

Talk about opposites – while dragons are often associated with evil, unicorns are symbols of all that is good and innocent. But they are also magical creatures that only wizards can see. Unicorns are much rarer than dragons because many have been killed for their horns. A unicorn's horn was once prized for its healing powers – it was believed that if

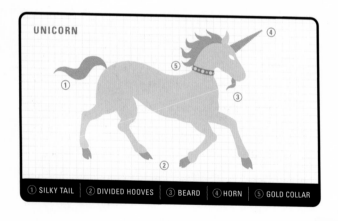

UNICORN

① SILKY TAIL ② DIVIDED HOOVES ③ BEARD ④ HORN ⑤ GOLD COLLAR

you drank from a unicorn's horn, you'd escape disease and be immune to poison. Since so many people hunted them for their horns, the unicorns went into hiding.

A unicorn is really a combination of a horse and a goat, but much more beautiful. It looks like a white horse, except for the single long horn growing from its forehead. A unicorn's tail is different from a horse's – thin, tufted and silky rather than bushy. Like a goat, a unicorn has a beard under its chin and its hooves are divided.

If you're ever lucky enough to spot one, you'll know that you've seen a unicorn from the beautiful gold collar around its neck. This collar is as valuable as a queen's crown jewels. Unicorns were once pets to royalty, and they are also considered royalty among animals. Treat the unicorn like the special being it is, and pet it like you'd pet your beloved familiar. In turn, the unicorn may send some luck your way.

CHAPTER SIX

A WIZARD'S RESOURCES

Merlin, Gandalf, Harry Potter, _____ .

That space is for your name. Go ahead and write it in! Now you're in the company of the most famous wizards in the world. Remember – knowing magic is a big responsibility. Use it for good and not for evil, and always keep this handbook around just in case you spot a dragon or someone sits on your pointy hat. Good luck!

FURTHER READING AND VIEWING

BOOKS

The Wonderful Wizard of Oz by L. Frank Baum (1900)

Bed-knobs and Broomsticks by Mary Norton (1943)

The Lion, the Witch and the Wardrobe by C. S. Lewis (1950)

Half Magic by Edward Eager (1954)

The Lord of the Rings by J. R. R. Tolkien (1954–1955)

The Phantom Tollbooth by Norton Juster (1961)

The Witches by Roald Dahl (1983)

The Lost Years of Merlin by T. A. Barron (1996)

Ella Enchanted by Gail Carson Levine (1997)

Harry Potter and the Philosopher's Stone by J. K. Rowling (1997)

FILMS

The Wizard of Oz, directed by Victor Fleming (1939)

A Connecticut Yankee in King Arthur's Court, directed by
Tay Garnett (1949)

The Witches of Eastwick, directed by George Miller (1987)

The Craft, directed by Andrew Fleming (1996)

Practical Magic, directed by Griffin Dunne (1998)

Harry Potter and the Philosopher's Stone, directed by Chris
Columbus (2001)

The Lord of the Rings trilogy, directed by Peter Jackson
(2001–2003)

GLOSSARY

* **Bewitch:** To cast a spell on someone or something

* **Bibliomancy:** The practice of using words in a book to predict the future

* **Cauldron:** A large, heavy pot in which wizards combine ingredients to make potions

* **Cleromancy:** The practice of throwing objects on to the ground and using the pattern of their fall to predict the future

* **Crystal ball:** A sphere of quartz crystal into which wizards gaze and see the future

* **Dragon:** A huge, scaly serpent with long claws (and sometimes monstrous wings)

* **Dream:** A series of thoughts, images and emotions which occur during sleep

* **Enchantment:** A spell

* **Familiar:** To a witch or wizard, a familiar is an animal companion that assists them during magic. To an ordinary person, 'familiar' is an adjective that means 'known, or easily recognized'.

* **Illusion:** Something that appears to be magic, but is really just a science-based trick

* **Magic circle:** An invisible circle made with a magic wand, inside which wizards practise magic, cast spells, stir potions, etc.

* **Magician:** Someone who creates illusions which may look like magic but are actually well-thought-out tricks

* **Omen:** An occurrence believed to predict a future event

* **Palmistry:** The practice of reading a person's character and future by the lines on his or her palms

* **Pestle and mortar:** A pestle is a short, chubby stick and a mortar is a sturdy bowl. A substance is ground into a powder when rubbed by a pestle into the bottom of a mortar.

* **Picture spell:** Every spell has a wish. The picture spell is an illustration of that wish.

* **Potion:** A liquid spell

* **Spell:** A series of words, possibly combined with a picture or a potion, created to seek the granting of a wish, whether it be making the broccoli disappear from your plate or getting an 'A' in your maths test.

* **Unicorn:** A mythical creature that is part-horse and part-goat, with a white coat and one long, spiralling horn

* **Wish:** Something that you want to happen

* **Wizard:** One who is skilled in magic

WIZARD'S NOTEBOOK

MY FAVOURITE WORD SPELLS

FOR DOING WELL IN A SCHOOL TEST OR PROJECT:

FOR IMPROVING THE WORLD AROUND ME:

FOR GETTING A GREAT BIRTHDAY PRESENT:

FOR GIVING GOOD LUCK TO A FRIEND:

FOR ANYTHING ELSE YOU WANT:

WIZARD IDENTIFICATION

SERVING ORDINARY
HUMANS SINCE 43 BC

The bearer of this card has read and understood *The Wizard's Handbook* and is hereby licensed to practise wizardry in countries throughout the world. Ownership of this ID certifies that the bearer is adept at predicting the future, communicating with animal familiars, and casting word spells and picture spells. The bearer of this card also pledges to use magic in ways that will benefit humanity and improve the world.